TABLE OF CONTENTS

What time is it?

Draw the hands on the clocks

Answer key included

#1

What time is it?

One hour increments.

#2

What time is it?

One hour increments.

#3

What time is it?

One hour increments.

#4

What time is it?

One hour increments.

#5

What time is it?

One hour increments.

#6

What time is it?

One hour increments.

#7

What time is it?

One hour increments.

#8

What time is it?

One hour increments.

#9

What time is it?

One hour increments.

What time is it?

One hour increments.

What time is it?

Half-hour increments.

#2

What time is it?

Half-hour increments.

#3

What time is it?

Half-hour increments.

#4

What time is it?

Half-hour increments.

What time is it?

Half-hour increments.

#6

What time is it?

Half-hour increments.

What time is it?

Half-hour increments.

#8

What time is it?

Half-hour increments.

#9

What time is it?

Half-hour increments.

#10

What time is it?

Half-hour increments.

#1

What time is it?

15 minute increments.

#2

What time is it?

15 minute increments.

#3

What time is it?

15 minute increments.

#4

What time is it?

15 minute increments.

#5

What time is it?

15 minute increments.

#6
What time is it?
15 minute increments.

#7

What time is it?

15 minute increments.

#8

What time is it?

15 minute increments.

What time is it?

15 minute increments.

#10

What time is it?

15 minute increments.

#1

What time is it?

5 minute increments.

#2
What time is it?
5 minute increments.

#3

What time is it?

5 minute increments.

#4

What time is it?

5 minute increments.

#5

What time is it?

5 minute increments.

What time is it?

5 minute increments.

What time is it?

5 minute increments.

What time is it?
5 minute increments.

#9

What time is it?

5 minute increments.

#10

What time is it?

5 minute increments.

#1

What time is it?

1 minute increments.

#2

What time is it?

1 minute increments.

#3

What time is it?

1 minute increments.

#4

What time is it?

1 minute increments.

What time is it?

1 minute increments.

#6

What time is it?

1 minute increments.

#7
What time is it?
1 minute increments.

What time is it?

1 minute increments.

#9

What time is it?

1 minute increments.

#10

What time is it?

1 minute increments.

#1

Draw the hands on the clocks
One hour increments.

6:00

4:00

8:00

12:00

2:00

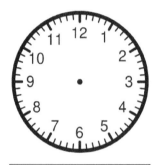

10:00

11:00

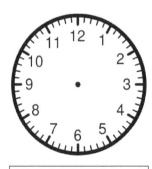

3:00

9:00

#2

Draw the hands on the clocks

One hour increments.

12:00

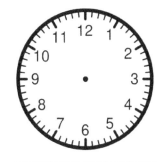

5:00

2:00

8:00

10:00

4:00

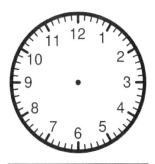

6:00

11:00

7:00

#3

Draw the hands on the clocks

One hour increments.

12:00

2:00

11:00

3:00

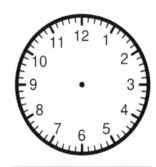

1:00

6:00

4:00

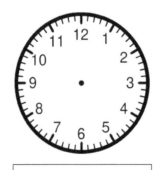

5:00

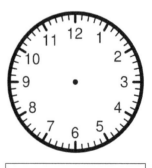

10:00

#4

Draw the hands on the clocks
One hour increments.

6:00

1:00

7:00

5:00

10:00

9:00

2:00

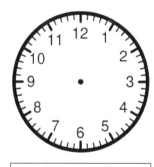

4:00

8:00

Draw the hands on the clocks
One hour increments.

5:00

4:00

6:00

10:00

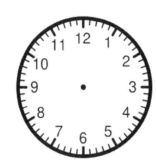

12:00

11:00

2:00

1:00

8:00

#6

Draw the hands on the clocks

One hour increments.

3:00

1:00

5:00

2:00

4:00

9:00

10:00

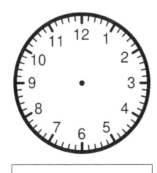

7:00

11:00

Draw the hands on the clocks
One hour increments.

10:00

4:00

1:00

6:00

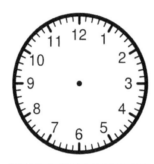

12:00

9:00

8:00

7:00

11:00

#8

Draw the hands on the clocks

One hour increments.

6:00

3:00

11:00

2:00

8:00

9:00

1:00

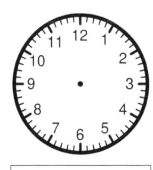

7:00

12:00

#9
Draw the hands on the clocks
One hour increments.

2:00

12:00

5:00

8:00

1:00

9:00

11:00

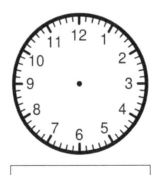

7:00

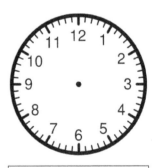

10:00

Draw the hands on the clocks
One hour increments.

12:00

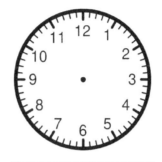

4:00

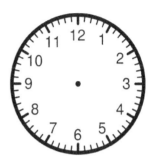

2:00

5:00

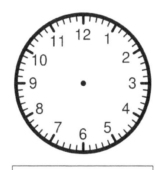

8:00

1:00

9:00

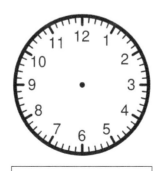

10:00

11:00

#1
Draw the hands on the clocks
Half-hour increments.

7:00

12:00

9:30

11:00

8:00

5:00

2:00

1:30

10:30

#2

Draw the hands on the clocks

Half-hour increments.

6:00

1:30

7:00

2:00

10:30

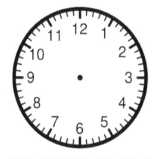

8:00

11:30

3:00

12:00

#3

Draw the hands on the clocks

Half-hour increments.

| 9:30 |

| 1:30 |

| 7:00 |

| 11:00 |

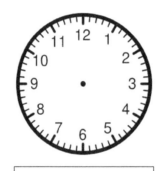

| 4:00 |

| 6:30 |

| 3:30 |

| 8:00 |

| 10:30 |

#4

Draw the hands on the clocks

Half-hour increments.

| 5:00 |

| 6:30 |

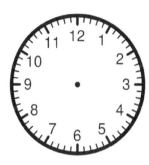

| 7:00 |

| 2:00 |

| 1:30 |

| 8:00 |

| 11:00 |

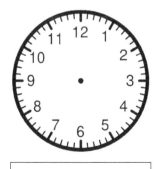

| 9:00 |

| 10:30 |

#5

Draw the hands on the clocks

Half-hour increments.

| 5:00 |

| 10:00 |

| 7:00 |

| 11:00 |

| 4:30 |

| 1:00 |

| 6:30 |

| 2:30 |

| 9:30 |

#6

Draw the hands on the clocks

Half-hour increments.

8:00

6:00

11:30

9:00

3:00

5:30

12:30

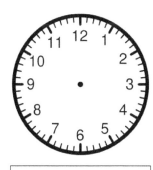

10:30

7:30

Draw the hands on the clocks

Half-hour increments.

| 12:30 |

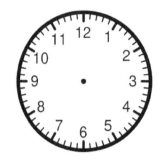

| 6:30 |

| 11:00 |

| 2:00 |

| 7:00 |

| 5:30 |

| 8:00 |

| 1:30 |

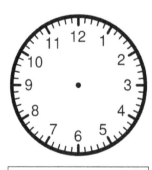

| 4:00 |

#8

Draw the hands on the clocks

Half-hour increments.

12:30

7:00

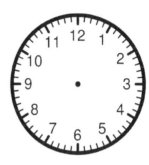

2:00

11:00

4:30

3:00

8:00

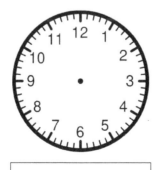

9:30

10:00

#9

Draw the hands on the clocks

Half-hour increments.

5:30

10:00

1:00

12:00

3:00

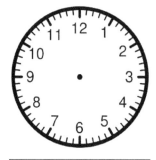

8:30

9:30

7:00

6:00

Draw the hands on the clocks

Half-hour increments.

9:30

11:00

6:00

8:30

3:30

10:00

1:00

12:30

5:30

#1
Draw the hands on the clocks
15 minute increments.

8:45

12:15

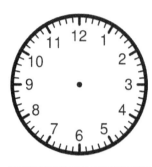

9:30

11:00

4:45

6:15

1:30

3:00

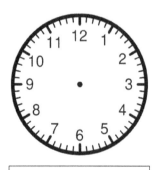

10:45

#2
Draw the hands on the clocks
15 minute increments.

1:45

12:00

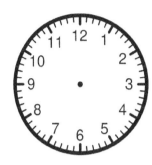

2:15

4:30

11:45

10:30

8:45

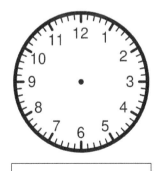

9:15

5:00

Draw the hands on the clocks
15 minute increments.

3:45

1:15

7:30

6:45

12:00

8:30

5:15

9:00

4:45

#4

Draw the hands on the clocks

15 minute increments.

3:15

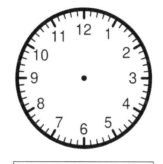

1:00

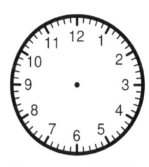

11:30

12:15

6:45

5:30

8:00

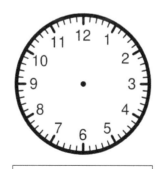

4:15

2:45

#5
Draw the hands on the clocks
15 minute increments.

9:00

6:30

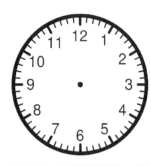

11:15

2:45

3:00

1:45

4:30

12:15

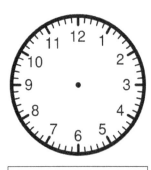

8:00

#6

Draw the hands on the clocks

15 minute increments.

10:30

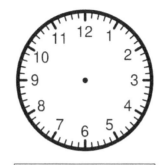

4:30

8:45

7:00

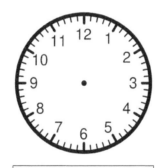

5:15

3:15

11:30

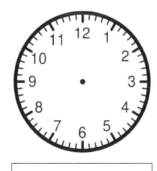

12:45

1:00

#7
Draw the hands on the clocks
15 minute increments.

3:30

11:00

2:15

4:45

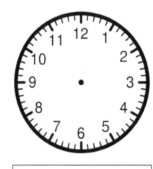

1:30

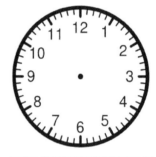

10:15

8:00

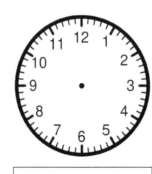

7:45

12:30

#8

Draw the hands on the clocks
15 minute increments.

12:00

1:15

4:00

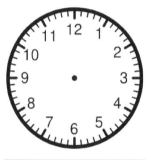

6:30

3:45

7:00

5:45

8:30

10:15

Draw the hands on the clocks
15 minute increments.

8:15

6:15

12:00

3:30

10:45

1:15

9:45

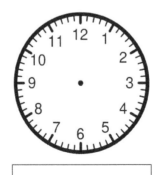

4:30

11:00

#10

Draw the hands on the clocks
15 minute increments.

3:30

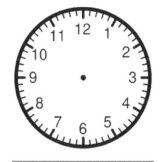

7:30

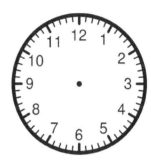

1:15

2:00

4:45

8:15

5:00

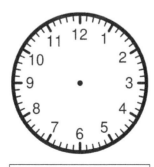

12:45

6:30

#1

Draw the hands on the clocks

5 minute increments.

7:10

5:00

9:25

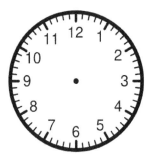

2:50

8:05

6:20

12:55

1:45

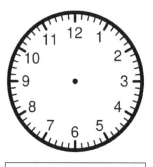

3:35

#2

Draw the hands on the clocks

5 minute increments.

2:05

10:15

5:40

1:10

4:30

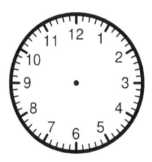

12:20

11:25

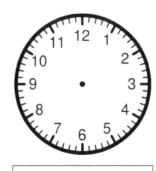

8:50

7:55

#3
Draw the hands on the clocks
5 minute increments.

12:05

5:35

6:30

10:50

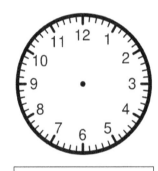

8:45

9:25

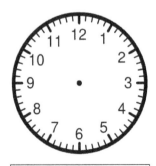

7:15

1:00

3:40

#4

Draw the hands on the clocks

5 minute increments.

3:30

12:20

8:00

2:40

1:55

10:25

6:50

7:15

9:35

#5

Draw the hands on the clocks

5 minute increments.

3:45

1:05

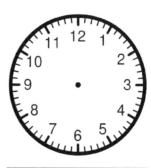

12:25

2:15

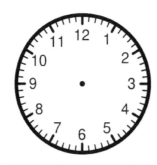

11:35

9:10

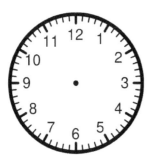

4:50

5:55

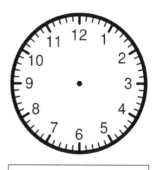

6:00

#6

Draw the hands on the clocks
5 minute increments.

9:45

11:15

2:50

10:25

8:55

5:10

12:30

7:35

1:40

Draw the hands on the clocks
5 minute increments.

12:20

5:45

1:55

3:50

9:40

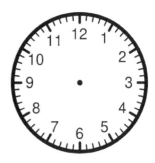

4:30

7:25

6:10

2:00

Draw the hands on the clocks
5 minute increments.

7:05

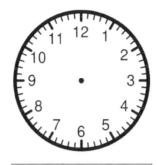

5:00

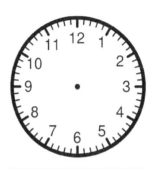

8:50

11:45

2:55

1:35

12:20

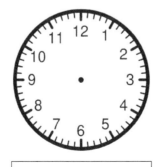

10:25

9:10

Draw the hands on the clocks

5 minute increments.

| 9:45 |

| 3:20 |

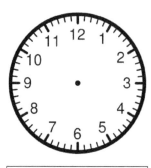

| 6:35 |

| 1:55 |

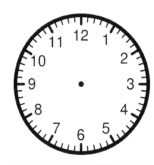

| 5:05 |

| 10:00 |

| 2:50 |

| 12:15 |

| 8:10 |

Draw the hands on the clocks
5 minute increments.

| 3:50 |

| 12:05 |

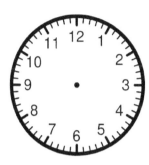

| 11:35 |

| 1:40 |

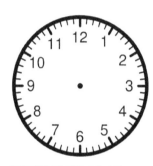

| 6:10 |

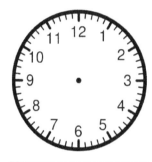

| 8:45 |

| 7:15 |

| 2:30 |

| 10:00 |

#1
Draw the hands on the clocks
1 minute increments.

5:02

10:53

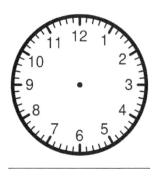

11:51

7:42

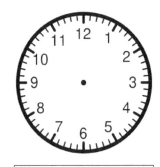

1:04

12:11

4:54

8:27

6:35

Draw the hands on the clocks
1 minute increments.

3:19

1:18

10:30

7:36

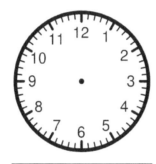

6:57

2:10

9:00

11:55

5:59

#3

Draw the hands on the clocks

1 minute increments.

8:17

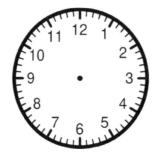

11:53

9:02

7:50

12:13

1:03

6:38

5:57

4:54

#4

Draw the hands on the clocks

1 minute increments.

12:00

3:39

9:53

4:11

7:35

2:28

11:40

8:33

5:57

#5

Draw the hands on the clocks

1 minute increments.

| 4:52 |

| 2:01 |

| 1:06 |

| 7:29 |

| 10:24 |

| 5:58 |

| 8:14 |

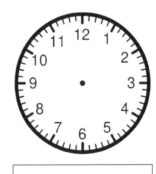

| 11:35 |

| 9:00 |

#6

Draw the hands on the clocks
1 minute increments.

11:15

10:07

4:24

5:27

7:55

6:21

1:45

12:08

9:00

Draw the hands on the clocks

1 minute increments.

10:23

4:15

11:58

9:22

8:40

3:05

1:11

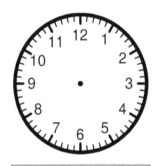

12:27

2:35

#8

Draw the hands on the clocks

1 minute increments.

| 1:56 |

| 7:50 |

| 4:34 |

| 3:49 |

| 5:19 |

| 2:30 |

| 12:53 |

| 9:59 |

| 11:15 |

#9
Draw the hands on the clocks
1 minute increments.

8:22

4:10

2:33

1:01

9:40

11:34

10:21

3:38

7:49

#10

Draw the hands on the clocks
1 minute increments.

4:04

7:51

10:31

5:50

2:09

3:48

11:58

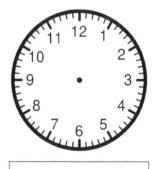

9:27

6:00

ANSWER KEY
What time is it?
One hour increments.

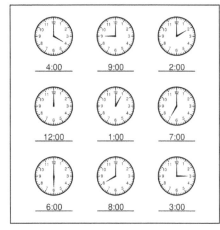

#1

4:00	9:00	2:00
12:00	1:00	7:00
6:00	8:00	3:00

#2

5:00	10:00	6:00
4:00	3:00	8:00
12:00	9:00	11:00

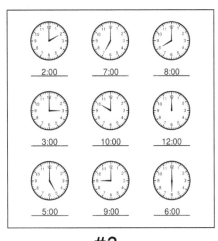

#3

2:00	7:00	8:00
3:00	10:00	12:00
5:00	9:00	6:00

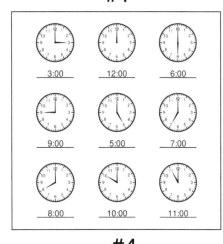

#4

3:00	12:00	6:00
9:00	5:00	7:00
8:00	10:00	11:00

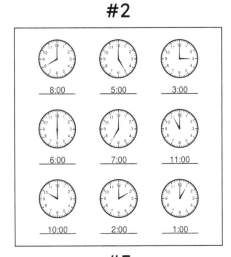

#5

8:00	5:00	3:00
6:00	7:00	11:00
10:00	2:00	1:00

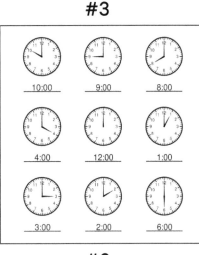

#6

10:00	9:00	8:00
4:00	12:00	1:00
3:00	2:00	6:00

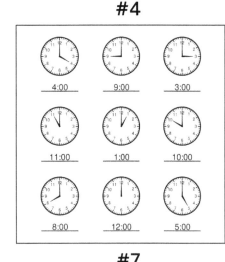

#7

4:00	9:00	3:00
11:00	1:00	10:00
8:00	12:00	5:00

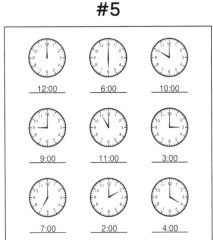

#8

12:00	6:00	10:00
9:00	11:00	3:00
7:00	2:00	4:00

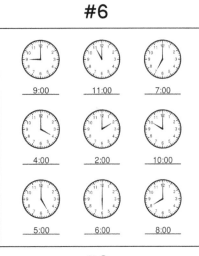

#9

9:00	11:00	7:00
4:00	2:00	10:00
5:00	6:00	8:00

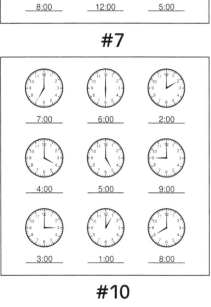

#10

7:00	6:00	2:00
4:00	5:00	9:00
3:00	1:00	8:00

ANSWER KEY
What time is it?
Half-hour increments.

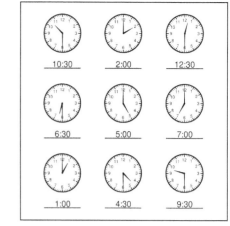

#1

10:30	2:00	12:30
6:30	5:00	7:00
1:00	4:30	9:30

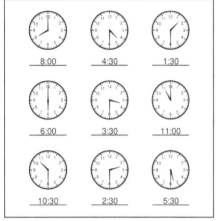

#2

8:00	4:30	1:30
6:00	3:30	11:00
10:30	2:30	5:30

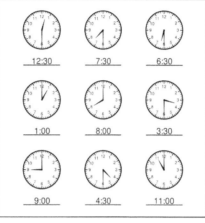

#3

12:30	7:30	6:30
1:00	8:00	3:30
9:00	4:30	11:00

#4

8:00	6:00	12:00
10:00	5:30	11:30
3:00	1:00	4:00

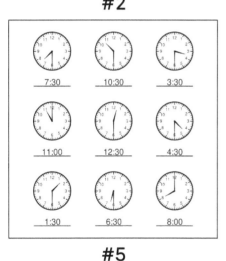

#5

7:30	10:30	3:30
11:00	12:30	4:30
1:30	6:30	8:00

#6

4:30	10:00	11:00
1:30	12:30	2:30
9:30	3:30	6:30

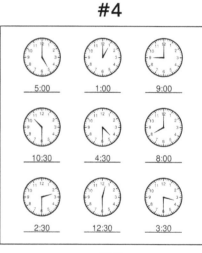

#7

5:00	1:00	9:00
10:30	4:30	8:00
2:30	12:30	3:30

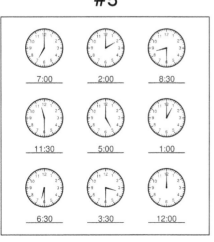

#8

7:00	2:00	8:30
11:30	5:00	1:00
6:30	3:30	12:00

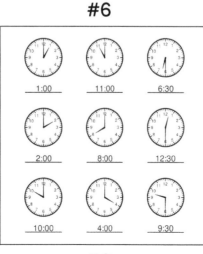

#9

1:00	11:00	6:30
2:00	8:00	12:30
10:00	4:00	9:30

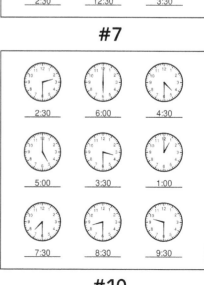

#10

2:30	6:00	4:30
5:00	3:30	1:00
7:30	8:30	9:30

ANSWER KEY
What time is it?
15 minute increments.

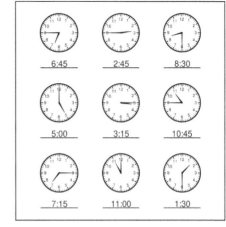

#1

6:45	2:45	8:30
5:00	3:15	10:45
7:15	11:00	1:30

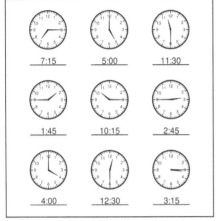

#2

7:15	5:00	11:30
1:45	10:15	2:45
4:00	12:30	3:15

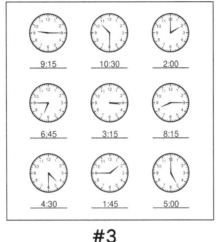

#3

9:15	10:30	2:00
6:45	3:15	8:15
4:30	1:45	5:00

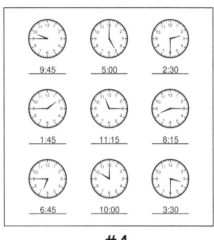

#4

9:45	5:00	2:30
1:45	11:15	8:15
6:45	10:00	3:30

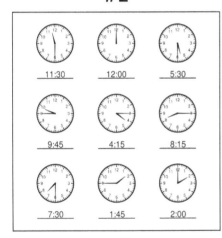

#5

11:30	12:00	5:30
9:45	4:15	8:15
7:30	1:45	2:00

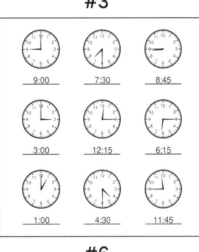

#6

9:00	7:30	8:45
3:00	12:15	6:15
1:00	4:30	11:45

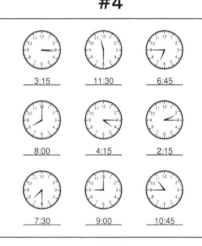

#7

3:15	11:30	6:45
8:00	4:15	2:15
7:30	9:00	10:45

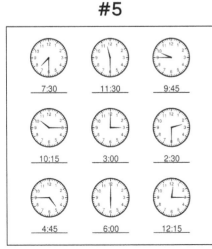

#8

7:30	11:30	9:45
10:15	3:00	2:30
4:45	6:00	12:15

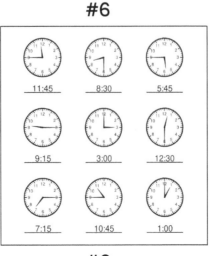

#9

11:45	8:30	5:45
9:15	3:00	12:30
7:15	10:45	1:00

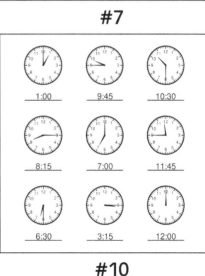

#10

1:00	9:45	10:30
8:15	7:00	11:45
6:30	3:15	12:00

ANSWER KEY
What time is it?
5 minute increments.

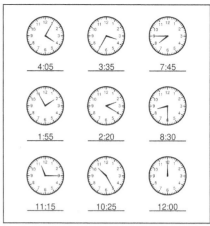

#1

4:05	3:35	7:45
1:55	2:20	8:30
11:15	10:25	12:00

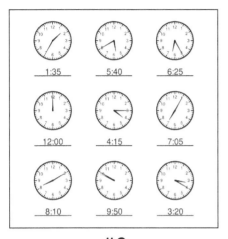

#2

1:35	5:40	6:25
12:00	4:15	7:05
8:10	9:50	3:20

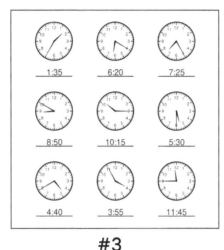

#3

1:35	6:20	7:25
8:50	10:15	5:30
4:40	3:55	11:45

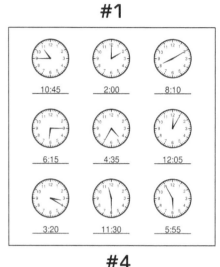

#4

10:45	2:00	8:10
6:15	4:35	12:05
3:20	11:30	5:55

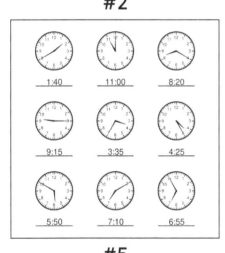

#5

1:40	11:00	8:20
9:15	3:35	4:25
5:50	7:10	6:55

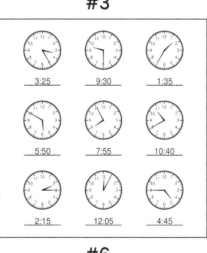

#6

3:25	9:30	1:35
5:50	7:55	10:40
2:15	12:05	4:45

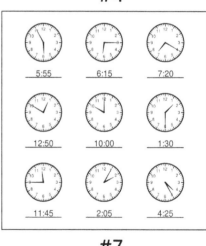

#7

5:55	6:15	7:20
12:50	10:00	1:30
11:45	2:05	4:25

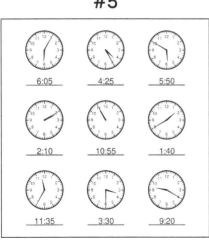

#8

6:05	4:25	5:50
2:10	10:55	1:40
11:35	3:30	9:20

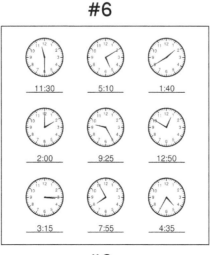

#9

11:30	5:10	1:40
2:00	9:25	12:50
3:15	7:55	4:35

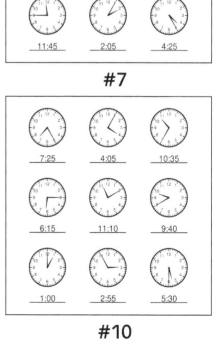

#10

7:25	4:05	10:35
6:15	11:10	9:40
1:00	2:55	5:30

ANSWER KEY
What time is it?
1 minute increments.

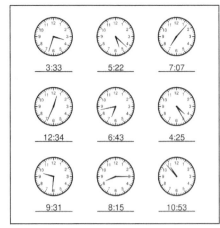

3:33   5:22   7:07

12:34   6:43   4:25

9:31   8:15   10:53

#1

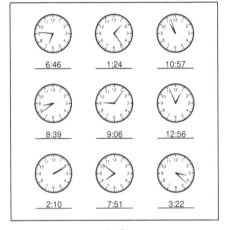

6:46   1:24   10:57

8:39   9:06   12:56

2:10   7:51   3:22

#2

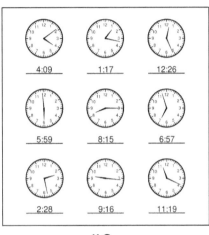

4:09   1:17   12:26

5:59   8:15   6:57

2:28   9:16   11:19

#3

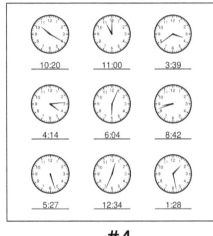

10:20   11:00   3:39

4:14   6:04   8:42

5:27   12:34   1:28

#4

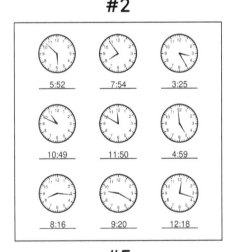

5:52   7:54   3:25

10:49   11:50   4:59

8:16   9:20   12:18

#5

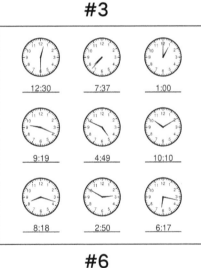

12:30   7:37   1:00

9:19   4:49   10:10

8:18   2:50   6:17

#6

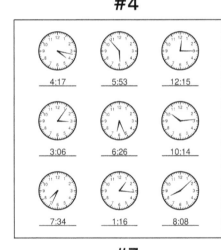

4:17   5:53   12:15

3:06   6:26   10:14

7:34   1:16   8:08

#7

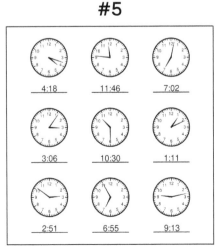

4:18   11:46   7:02

3:06   10:30   1:11

2:51   6:55   9:13

#8

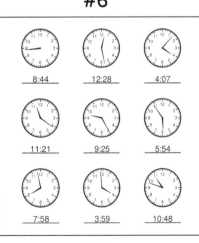

8:44   12:28   4:07

11:21   9:25   5:54

7:58   3:59   10:48

#9

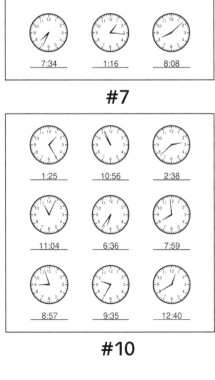

1:25   10:56   2:38

11:04   6:36   7:59

8:57   9:35   12:40

#10

ANSWER KEY
Draw the hands on the clocks
One hour increments.

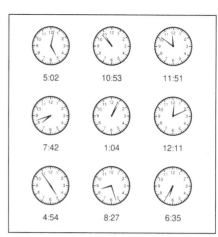

5:02   10:53   11:51
7:42   1:04   12:11
4:54   8:27   6:35

#1

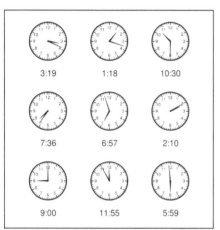

3:19   1:18   10:30
7:36   6:57   2:10
9:00   11:55   5:59

#2

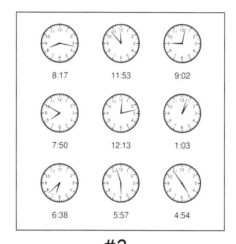

8:17   11:53   9:02
7:50   12:13   1:03
6:38   5:57   4:54

#3

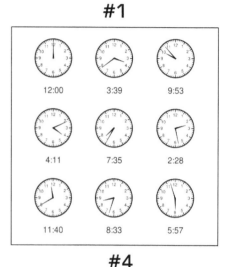

12:00   3:39   9:53
4:11   7:35   2:28
11:40   8:33   5:57

#4

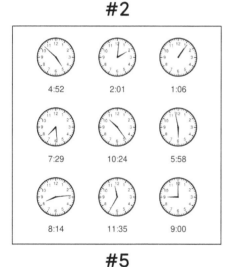

4:52   2:01   1:06
7:29   10:24   5:58
8:14   11:35   9:00

#5

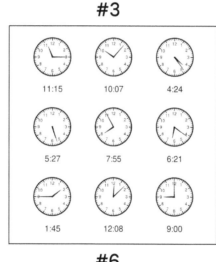

11:15   10:07   4:24
5:27   7:55   6:21
1:45   12:08   9:00

#6

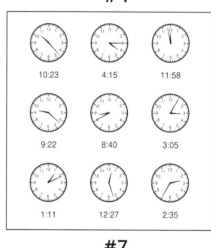

10:23   4:15   11:58
9:22   8:40   3:05
1:11   12:27   2:35

#7

1:56   7:50   4:34
3:49   5:19   2:30
12:53   9:59   11:15

#8

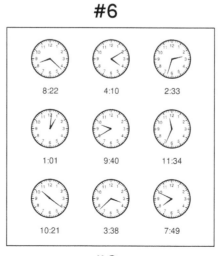

8:22   4:10   2:33
1:01   9:40   11:34
10:21   3:38   7:49

#9

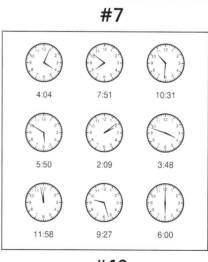

4:04   7:51   10:31
5:50   2:09   3:48
11:58   9:27   6:00

#10

ANSWER KEY
Draw the hands on the clocks
Half-hour increments.

#1

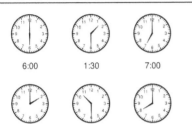

#2

#3

#4

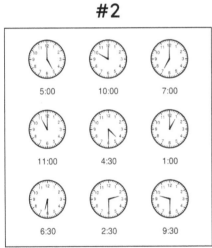

#5

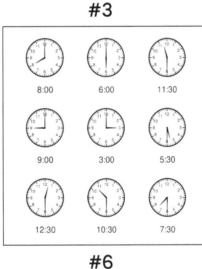

#6

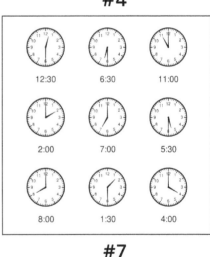

#7

#8

#9

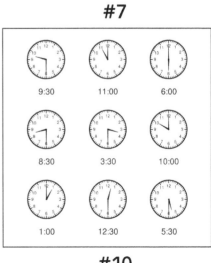

#10

ANSWER KEY
Draw the hands on the clocks
15 minute increments.

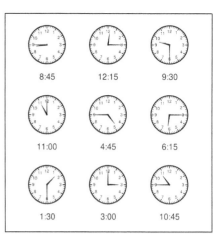

8:45   12:15   9:30

11:00   4:45   6:15

1:30   3:00   10:45

#1

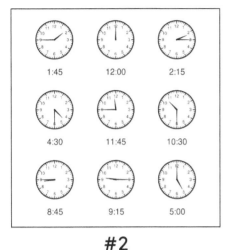

1:45   12:00   2:15

4:30   11:45   10:30

8:45   9:15   5:00

#2

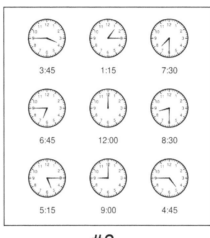

3:45   1:15   7:30

6:45   12:00   8:30

5:15   9:00   4:45

#3

3:15   1:00   11:30

12:15   6:45   5:30

8:00   4:15   2:45

#4

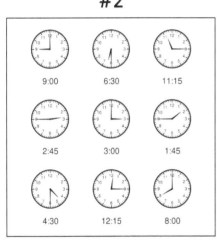

9:00   6:30   11:15

2:45   3:00   1:45

4:30   12:15   8:00

#5

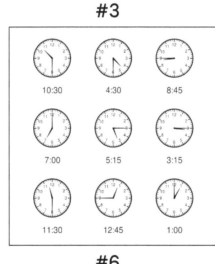

10:30   4:30   8:45

7:00   5:15   3:15

11:30   12:45   1:00

#6

3:30   11:00   2:15

4:45   1:30   10:15

8:00   7:45   12:30

#7

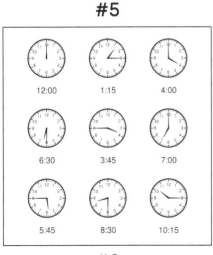

12:00   1:15   4:00

6:30   3:45   7:00

5:45   8:30   10:15

#8

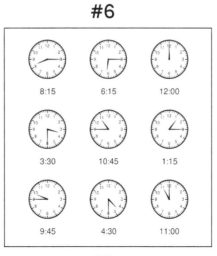

8:15   6:15   12:00

3:30   10:45   1:15

9:45   4:30   11:00

#9

3:30   7:30   1:15

2:00   4:45   8:15

5:00   12:45   6:30

#10

ANSWER KEY
Draw the hands on the clocks
5 minute increments.

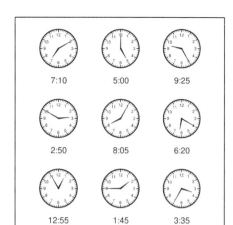

7:10	5:00	9:25
2:50	8:05	6:20
12:55	1:45	3:35

#1

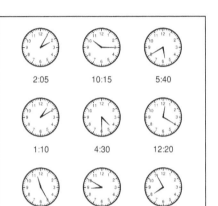

2:05	10:15	5:40
1:10	4:30	12:20
11:25	8:50	7:55

#2

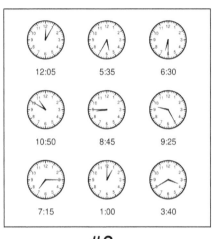

12:05	5:35	6:30
10:50	8:45	9:25
7:15	1:00	3:40

#3

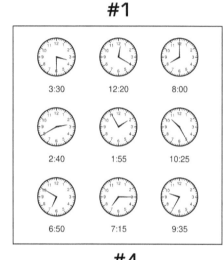

3:30	12:20	8:00
2:40	1:55	10:25
6:50	7:15	9:35

#4

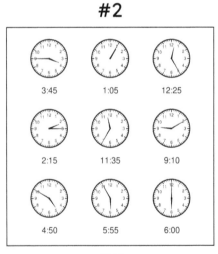

3:45	1:05	12:25
2:15	11:35	9:10
4:50	5:55	6:00

#5

9:45	11:15	2:50
10:25	8:55	5:10
12:30	7:35	1:40

#6

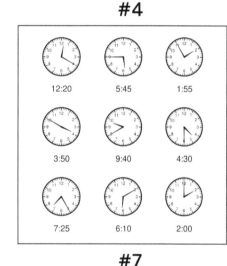

12:20	5:45	1:55
3:50	9:40	4:30
7:25	6:10	2:00

#7

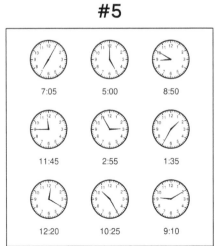

7:05	5:00	8:50
11:45	2:55	1:35
12:20	10:25	9:10

#8

9:45	3:20	6:35
1:55	5:05	10:00
2:50	12:15	8:10

#9

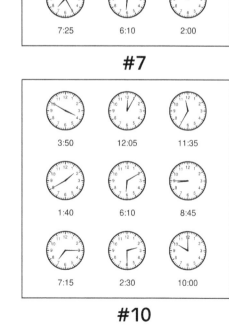

3:50	12:05	11:35
1:40	6:10	8:45
7:15	2:30	10:00

#10

ANSWER KEY
Draw the hands on the clocks
1 minute increments.

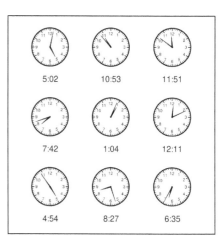

5:02   10:53   11:51

7:42   1:04   12:11

4:54   8:27   6:35

#1

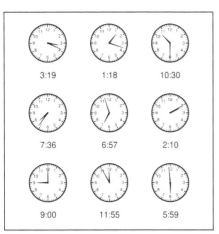

3:19   1:18   10:30

7:36   6:57   2:10

9:00   11:55   5:59

#2

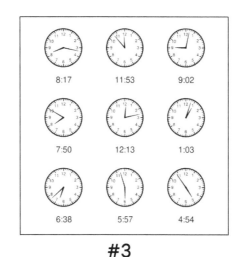

8:17   11:53   9:02

7:50   12:13   1:03

6:38   5:57   4:54

#3

12:00   3:39   9:53

4:11   7:35   2:28

11:40   8:33   5:57

#4

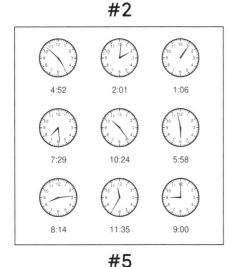

4:52   2:01   1:06

7:29   10:24   5:58

8:14   11:35   9:00

#5

11:15   10:07   4:24

5:27   7:55   6:21

1:45   12:08   9:00

#6

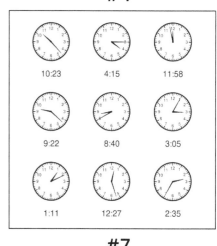

10:23   4:15   11:58

9:22   8:40   3:05

1:11   12:27   2:35

#7

1:56   7:50   4:34

3:49   5:19   2:30

12:53   9:59   11:15

#8

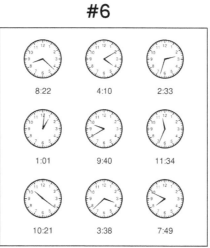

8:22   4:10   2:33

1:01   9:40   11:34

10:21   3:38   7:49

#9

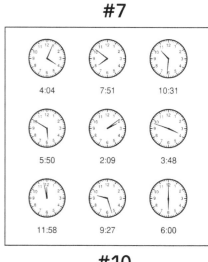

4:04   7:51   10:31

5:50   2:09   3:48

11:58   9:27   6:00

#10

CPSIA information can be obtained
at www.ICGtesting.com
Printed in the USA
BVHW021019110523
664004BV00017B/87